Bob the Builder

This Bob the Builder Annual belongs to

....

Age ....

When I grow up I'd like to be

....

Bob the Builder™

ANNUAL 2012

EGMONT
We bring stories to life

First published in Great Britain 2011
by Egmont UK Limited
239 Kensington High Street, London W8 6SA
Written by Jane Riordan • Designed by Anthony Duke • Photography by Beth Harwood

ISBN 978 1 4052 5810 4
1 3 5 7 9 10 8 6 4 2
Printed in Italy

Contents

Meet the Team! 8

Lofty and the Diggers Three 10

Lofty Introduces ... the Diplodocus 16

Strange Happenings 18

Artists in Action 19

Scoop and the Roller Coaster 20

Scoop Introduces ... the Tyrannosaurus Rex 26

Which Rubble? 28

Hammer Away! 29

Rubble and the Seagull Surprise 30

Dizzy Introduces ... the Pterodactyl 34

Make Your Own Scrambler! 36

Roley's Impossible Bump 38

Roley Introduces ... the Triceratops 44

Colour Mix-up 46

Make Your Own Triceratops 48

Hide-and-Seek 50

Scoop's Dino Dodge 51

Muck's Train Trouble 52

Muck Introduces ... the Stegosaurus 56

Animal Antics 58

Roller Coaster Whizz! 59

A Dinosaur for Scratch 60

Fun Park Race! 66

Answers 68

Meet the Team!

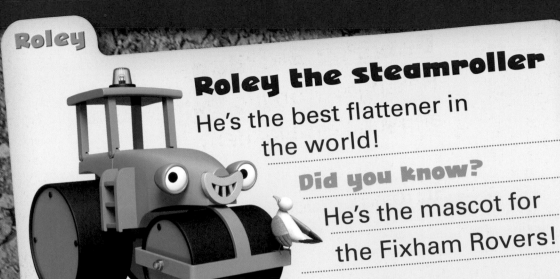

Roley the steamroller

He's the best flattener in the world!

Did you know?

He's the mascot for the Fixham Rovers!

Scoop

Scoop the digger

He's full of big ideas.

Did you know?

He's the first machine Bob ever owned!

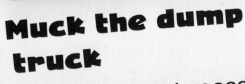

Muck

Muck the dump truck

He loves to get messy!

Did you know?

He's one of the Diggers Three, with Scoop and Scratch.

Bob the Builder

He's hard-working, enthusiastic and a natural leader.

Did you know?

He loves cheese sandwiches!

Scratch the small digger

He's the baby of Bob's team.

Did you know?

He needs to take a nap each day!

Dizzy the cement mixer

She's excitable and very keen.

Did you know?

She loves to solve a puzzle.

9

Lofty and the Diggers Three

Scoop, Muck and Scratch were in a good mood. They raced around, bashing their diggers together, calling out, **"Who are we!? The Diggers Three! Scoop and Muck and Little Scratchie!"**

Lofty looked on longingly; he wished he was in the Diggers Three.

He didn't have long to feel sad because Bob had gathered the whole machine team together to tell them about an exciting new building job.

The team had been asked to build a whole park full of rides and games for children. Tony Toberomi was going to help them, as he had built lots of parks before.

Bob introduced Tony to the team. Tony told them all about the park.

"There'll be a roller coaster, a train ride and a flying ride. But before we can build anything we have

to move the hills that are there now, and make the ground flat."

"That will mean loads of earth to carry away," said Muck.

"There's a new machine here to help!" announced Bob. **"Everyone, meet Rubble!"**

Rubble, the giant dumper truck, couldn't wait to start work. But Lofty was sad – now Rubble would be in the digger club, too. All the work seemed to be about digging. He didn't think Bob would need him at all.

Before the diggers set to work, Tony Toberomi gave them one last job.

"Every park needs a theme. Can you help me come up with an idea?"

The Diggers Three thought they were very clever and were sure to come up with an idea. Lofty decided to have his own idea so the Diggers Three would think *he* was really clever and let him join in.

Lofty went off to think of a theme. He saw Mr Bentley in his garden, surrounded by flowers.

"Oh! The park could have a flower theme!" thought Lofty.

And he borrowed some flowers to show the Diggers Three.

"They'll think I'm clever enough to join their club when they hear my idea," said Lofty.

But when he got to Muck and the others, he saw Scratch holding some flowers already.

Disappointed, Lofty went off to look for more ideas. He met Dickie Olivier wearing a wonderful pirate costume.

"A pirate theme!" thought Lofty to himself. **"I'll borrow this hat to show the Diggers Three."**

But when Lofty got back to the diggers he heard Muck say, **"Shiver my timbers! Walk the plank!"** Lofty sighed – they had already

thought of the pirate idea. But, in fact, the diggers hadn't thought of any ideas at all, they were just playing.

Lofty went towards the sea, still trying to think of a theme for the park.

"Oh, the sea!" he thought suddenly, "the park could have a seaside theme!" He borrowed a surfboard, to bring back to the others, to explain his idea.

Back at the site all the hills had been flattened, except for one. The diggers had been working hard but they hadn't had a single idea for the park. "I thought diggers were clever," said Scoop, "but we haven't come up with anything." Bob told them not to worry. He reminded them that it wasn't easy coming up with big ideas.

The Diggers Three thought that being near the sea would help them to think of an idea. As Lofty came back he heard them talking about the sea. "They've already thought of all my ideas. They're so clever," said Lofty to himself, sadly. "I'll never be in the Diggers Three." He rolled away but Rubble saw him leaving and went after him.

"What's the matter, Lofty?" Rubble asked.

"I wanted to be in the Diggers club, like you. But I'm not clever enough," replied Lofty.

Rubble led Lofty back to the site and the diggers explained to him about the club. **"The Diggers Three isn't a real club,"** said Scratch. **"It's just a silly name we made up. We're not clever, we couldn't think of any ideas for the park."**

"But you thought of the same ones as me: flowers, pirates and the seaside," said Lofty, surprised.

The diggers thought they were great ideas and wished that they really had thought of them. But before the park could have a theme, the team needed to flatten the last hill. It was full of huge stones and was difficult to dig.

The diggers asked Lofty to help lift out the rocks. As the team worked together to clear the earth from around the rocks they realised, to their surprise, that these weren't just ordinary rocks – they were part of an enormous skeleton! Spud had borrowed a big book from the museum and it told him that this was the skeleton of a Diplodocus – a dinosaur!

"Maybe that's what the park's theme could be," suggested Lofty.

"Yes," replied Tony Toberomi, **"Fixham's Dinosaur Fun Park!"**

Everyone agreed it was an excellent idea.

"Now you're in an even better club than the Diggers Three," laughed Scoop. **"The dinosaur club!"** Everyone cheered and Scratch hoped to himself that, if there were more dinosaurs to be found, he'd be as clever as Lofty and find the next one!

Er ... I wouldn't want to meet this big dino on a dark night, or even in the daytime! He looks a bit like me, though, with his long, long body!

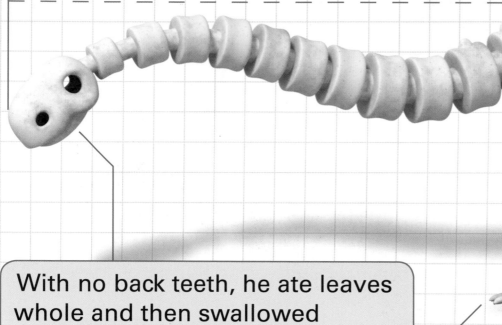

With no back teeth, he ate leaves whole and then swallowed stones to help grind them!

This dinosaur only ate plants.

He was lighter than other dinosaurs because his bones were hollow.

the Diplodocus

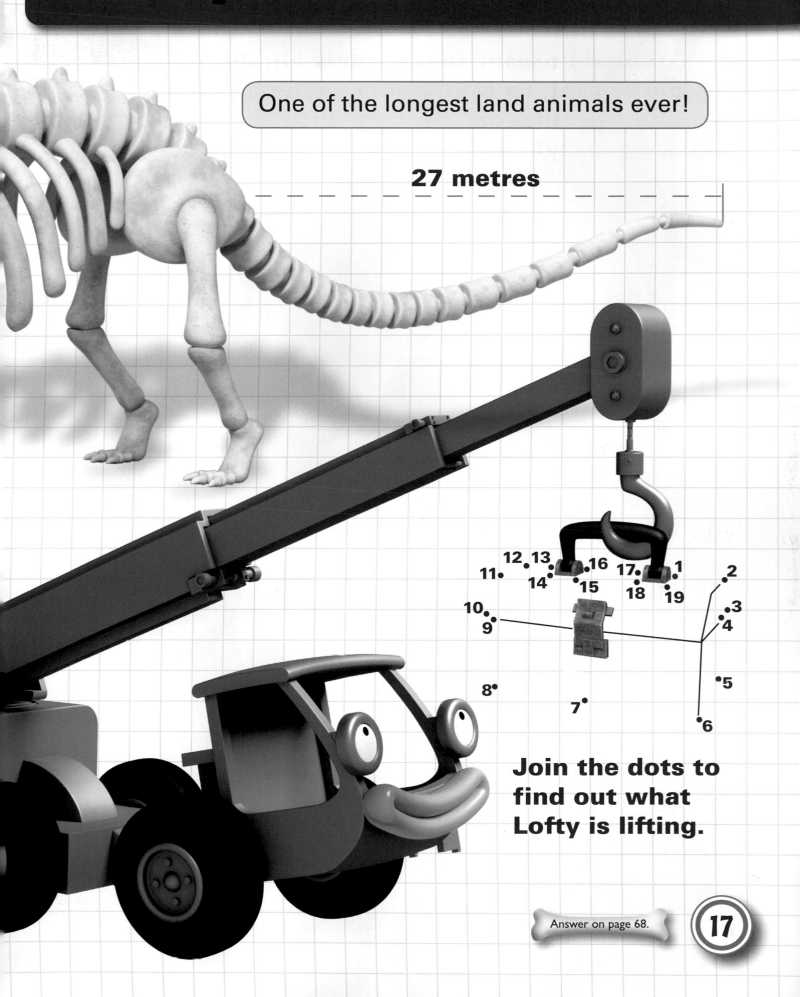

One of the longest land animals ever!

27 metres

Join the dots to find out what Lofty is lifting.

Answer on page 68.

17

Strange Happenings

All is not as it should be in Fixham Harbour. Can you spot the 5 things that have gone wrong in this picture?

Answers on page 68.

Artists in Action

The artist David Mockney is painting Bob's portrait. Can you help him to finish it? Why not add a beard or glasses to make it into a funny face?

Scoop and the Roller Coaster

Scoop was busy looking at the big book of dinosaurs. Scratch was impressed. If Scoop was clever enough to read a book like that he would be able to find another dinosaur!

"Well ..." said Scoop, "I probably could, now that I know all about them."

Just then, Bob came to tell the team that today they would be building a roller coaster for the Fun Park.

"Ooh, a ride that goes up and down and round and round ... I love roller coasters!" said Wendy, excitedly.

Bob looked a bit worried. He wasn't so sure about all the up and down and round and round! But there was too much work to do to think about it any more. There were the foundations to dig, supports to cement in, tracks to lay, a platform to build and, last of all, the carriages to put in place.

"Great," said Scratch, "let's start digging! And I really hope I find a dinosaur today!"

"You will if you stick with me," said Scoop. "Remember, I've read all about it."

At the Fun Park, Scoop was still boasting.

"Rule one," he said, "is look for clues." And he sent the rest of the team off to get started.

"Rule two," Scoop continued, as Rubble rumbled by with a big load of earth, "is dinosaur hunters should search through earth for bones. Tip it out, Rubble!"

"But, Scoop … Packer's coming with the carriages," said Dizzy, anxiously.

Rubble didn't look sure about tipping out the earth, but Scoop said he knew best so Rubble did as Scoop said.

At that moment, Packer arrived.

"What's going on?" he said. "I can't get through with the carriages." But just then Scoop noticed a small hill.

"Rule three," he said, excitedly, "is dinosaur hunters dig up hills. It said so in the book."

"But what about all this earth?" said Rubble.

Scoop told Rubble to look through the earth while he went to investigate the hill. Scoop wanted them to start digging right away, but Muck thought they ought to ask Bob first.

"I've read the book," explained Scoop, "so I know best."

Muck dug a big chunk out of the middle of the hill. Tony Toberomi saw what he was doing.

"Stop!" he shouted. "What are you doing to my beautiful landscape?"

Muck said he was very sorry and would put the hill back the way it was. Scoop was too busy thinking about dinosaurs to listen or help.

"We could find another hill, somewhere else," he said to himself.

A little later, Wendy was unpacking boxes of rocks and showing them to Tony Toberomi. They were fake rocks to decorate the Fun Park. Wendy put them to one side and went to help Bob build the loading platform.

Scoop spotted the pile of rocks.

"Rocks!" he said. **"Rule four is to look for dinosaur bones … inside rocks!"**

Muck didn't look sure. He picked one up and noticed it was very light.

"Maybe they're for something special," he suggested.

"I know best, Muck," said Scoop. **"Let's crack them open!"**

Together, they raised their buckets and smashed them down onto the rocks! The rocks broke into pieces. They were hollow!

"These aren't real rocks!" said Scrambler. **"They must be special pretend ones for decoration …"**

"Maybe we should stop dinosaur hunting now, Scoop," said Muck, worried.

But Scoop wasn't listening. All he could think about was finding another dinosaur. He was surprised when he suddenly realised that the others had all gone. He looked down at the broken rocks.

"Maybe I don't know best after all," he said, sadly. **"I didn't even read the book properly and now my friends don't want to find dinosaurs with me."**

At the roller coaster, Lofty was lifting the last carriage into place. Scoop joined the others and explained how he had wanted to show that he knew how to find a dinosaur but that all he'd done was cause trouble.

"I'm sorry," he said. **"I forgot the most important rule of all – always listen to your friends!"**

Then Scoop had the idea to go and find some more rocks to replace the ones he'd broken.

"We can look wherever you think is best!" he said to the team. They all followed Scratch who knew a good rocky place. Together the team lifted out rocks until there was only one left.

"That must be yours then, Scoop," said Scratch.

Scoop tried to lift the rock but it wouldn't budge. He dug around the edges. It looked a funny shape.

"I think you've found a dinosaur!" shouted Scratch, excitedly.

Spud took a look in his book. **"You've found a T. Rex,"** he announced.

Scoop had a very good idea what to do with the dinosaur – he'd put it under the track of the roller coaster!

It was time to give the roller coaster a test run. Wendy, Bob, Tony and some children climbed into the carriages. Slowly the ride clunked into action. Bob closed his eyes! Everyone screamed with excitement as they whizzed down the T. Rex's back and round the track!

"That was amazing, wasn't it, Bob?" said Wendy.

But Bob was looking rather green as he staggered off the ride.

"Yes … it was great … just great," he said, weakly.

"You know what else is great?" said Scratch. **"Dinosaurs – and next time I'm going to find one!"**

Scoop Introduces ...

The most famous of all the dinosaurs looks a bit like me, don't you think? His jaws are big and strong, like my scoop!

A fierce meat-eating dinosaur

His head could be as big as an adult person.

His short arms couldn't reach his mouth!

This dinosaur was able to sprint short distances as fast as an Olympic athlete!

the Tyrannosaurus Rex

Find your brightest yellow crayon to colour Scoop.

Which Rubble?

Rubble, the big, new dumper truck, can't hide easily but can you match the picture of Rubble to the correct shadow?

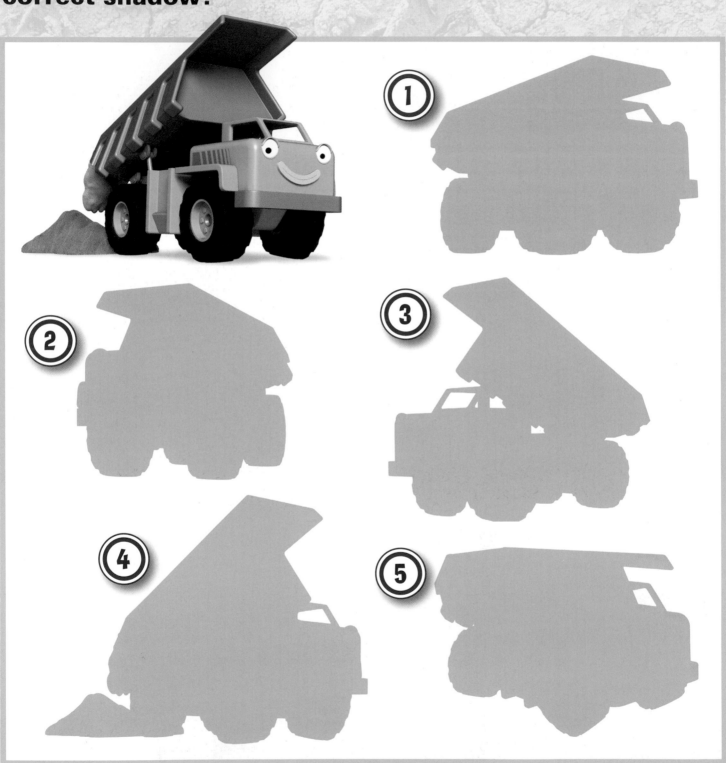

Answer on page 68.

Hammer Away!

Bob the Builder always likes to have his hammer nearby – he never knows when he might need it. Are there enough hammers to be sure that each Bob will have one?

Answer on page 68.

Rubble and the Seagull Surprise

Bob   **Dizzy**   **Rubble**   **seagull**   **mud**

You can help read this story. Join in when you see a picture.

 and the team were building a flying ride. "Spinny and

fast just like me!" said . "The team are all fast,"

thought  , "except for me." At the site

needed someone fast to pick up the plans for the

carriages. "I'll go. I'll be really fast," said  and

he rushed off. But he was in so much of a hurry that, on

the way back, he dropped the plans, and a  flew

off with them!

 hurried after the – he didn't want the

team to think he was slow. But 's rushing

caused accidents.  got stuck in a pile of .

The  dropped the plans but they got covered

in 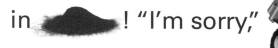! "I'm sorry,"  said. "I wanted to be fast."

"You may not be fast," replied , "but you are big and

strong and we love having you on the team." Just then

 noticed something in the – a bone.

The team dug and found a Pterodactyl – a flying reptile!

 didn't need the plans now. They had a great new

name for the ride – **the Pterodactyl Express!**

Dizzy Introduces ...

Wow! This flying reptile was around at the same time as the dinosaurs – brilliant! I wonder if it whizzed around as fast as me!

The wings were made of a leathery material.

Some had no teeth at all!

Pterodactyls ate large insects.

Their bones were hollow and filled with air.

These two pictures of Dizzy and Bob may look the same but there are 5 differences in picture 2. Can you spot them all?

Answer on page 68.

Make Your Own Scrambler!

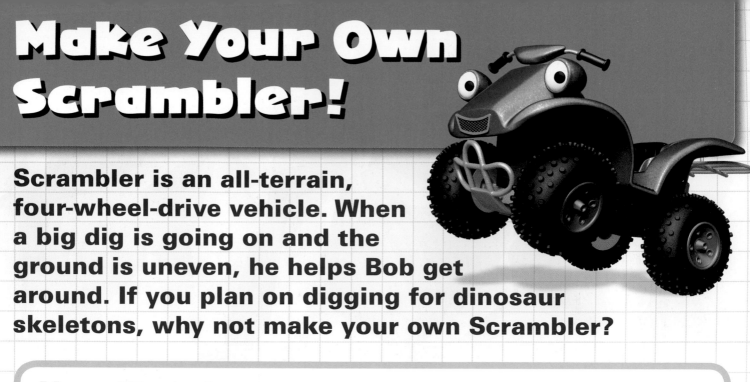

Scrambler is an all-terrain, four-wheel-drive vehicle. When a big dig is going on and the ground is uneven, he helps Bob get around. If you plan on digging for dinosaur skeletons, why not make your own Scrambler?

You will need:
A large cardboard box, extra cardboard, a long paper tube, aluminium foil, black and blue card, scissors, paint, glue.

1

Ask an adult to help you shape a **cardboard box** as shown.

2 **Paint** it, inside and out, in a bright **Scrambler blue.**

3 Tyres can be cut out of card and painted. The **radiator plate** and **luggage rack** are just made out of card covered in aluminium foil. Glue them in place.

4 To make the **handlebars,** cover a cardboard tube in aluminium foil. Wrap strips of black paper or card around the 2 ends and stick small discs of black card, just a little larger than the tube, over each end.

5 Glue the handlebars into a looped-over piece of blue card. Then glue the blue card to the box.

Now jump in and scram!

Roley's Impossible Bump

Roley and Scratch were getting to know each other a bit better.

"**I bet you could flatten anything, Roley,**" said Scratch.

"**Well, maybe,**" replied Roley.

"**Hills, ridges, lumps and bumps,**" continued Scratch.

"**Oh, I could flatten those. So, yes, I guess I could flatten anything,**" said Roley, thoughtfully.

"**You're the best, Roley,**" said Scratch.

They were interrupted by Bob and Wendy calling the team together. Bob announced that they were going to build a slide at the Fun Park today. Tony Toberomi told them that Mr Bentley was coming later to check that everything was safe.

"Well, there won't be any lumps or bumps," said Scratch. **"Roley can flatten anything."**

Bob thought it was a good idea to get Roley to flatten the ground, as it was rather bumpy. He asked Roley to flatten any bumps that children could trip over.

While the rest of the team started working on the slide, Roley set to work.

Scratch watched Roley. **"You're the best flattener in the whole world,"** he said.

"Rock and roll, Scratchie!" he replied. **"Right then! I'm off to flatten everything!"** Roley rushed off flattening all the little bumps he could find. But it wasn't long before he found a big one.

"Another bump to be flattened by the world's best flattener!" he cried.

Bird flew down and watched Roley roll over the lump again and again. But the bump was still there!

Roley was very upset. **"How can I be the best flattener in the world if I can't flatten this silly bump?"** he said. **"And what if Mr Bentley finds it – I'll have to make sure no one sees it. And I can't tell Scratch. If he finds out there's a bump I can't flatten, he won't think I'm the best flattener in the world!"**

Meanwhile, Bob and the rest of the team were working on the slide. Muck rolled away from the others to get the rails for the slide stairs. Roley was worried Muck was going to go close to the bump and see it.

"You can't go this way, Muck!" he said, quickly. And he sent him round a different way.

"Oh, OK," said Muck, a little surprised. **"Are you all right, Roley?"**

But Roley had already rushed off to try to flatten the bump again. No matter how hard he tried he couldn't do it.

Back at the build Lofty was lowering the slide into position.

"Careful, Lofty," said Packer. **"The road here is bumpy and the slide has moved a bit."**

"Roley could flatten the road," said Scratch, proudly. **"He can flatten anything!"**

Bob thought that was a good idea. He called Roley over to flatten the road. Roley worked as quickly as he could because he didn't want to leave his big bump for anyone to find! Roley rushed back to the bump –  but he was too late! Scratch was already there.

"Scratch! I've got something to tell you," Roley admitted. **"I'm not the best flattener in the world because I can't flatten this bump here …"**

"Oh …" said Scratch. **"But you are the best flattener in the world, Roley! If you can't flatten this bump on your own, then no one can!"**

That cheered Roley up and gave him a good idea. Maybe with help from the team he could flatten the bump.

Meanwhile, Bob and the team had finished the slide. It looked great but Bob was worried.

"It's not very dinosaur-y," he said.

As they were talking about the problem, Roley rushed up and told them all about the bump he couldn't flatten.

"That's OK, Roley! We can help!" said Bob and together they all went to look at Roley's bump. Roley showed them how rolling the ground just wouldn't make it flat but as he rolled, some earth

came away and Scoop spotted something white underneath.

Spud was pretty sure it was a dinosaur bone.

"No wonder you couldn't flatten it, Roley!" said Bob. **"Let's get digging!"**

All the team set to work and before too long they had unearthed a huge dinosaur. Spud looked in his book and announced to everyone that it was a Triceratops!

Mr Bentley was delighted to see that the team had found another dinosaur and he was also very pleased with how flat the rest of the park was looking.

"That was Roley!" said Scratch. **"He's the best flattener in the world!"**

"Aw, thanks, everyone," said Roley, embarrassed. **"And I've got an idea where we can put my dinosaur – under the slide!"**

The team put the dinosaur in place. It looked amazing and the children loved it!

"Top marks, everybody," said Mr Bentley. **"Especially Roley!"**

Scratch just hoped that it would be his turn to find a dinosaur next.

Roley Introduces ...

This Triceratops has got some serious flattening power – just like me! Rock and roll!

Not one, not two, but three horns!

This big bone is called a frill.

The Triceratops looks a lot like the modern-day rhinoceros!

Triceratops was a plant-eating dinosaur.

44

the Triceratops

Can you match the picture of Roley to the correct shadow?

Answer on page 68. **45**

Colour Mix-up

Spud has given the machine team a new lick of paint. But there's been a bit of a mix-up. Shout out the name of each machine in turn and then point to the paint pot that should have been used to paint them.

Answers on page 68.

Make Your Own Triceratops

1 **Trace over** or photocopy the dinosaur outline. Colour your dinosaur and his frill.

You will need:
Paper, crayons, scissors, glue

2 Ask an adult to **cut out** the dinosaur and frill.

3 Ask an adult to **cut along** the blue lines to separate the legs. Fold along all the dotted lines. The legs should be folded inwards to help the dinosaur to stand.

4 **Glue** the 2 sides of the head together.

5 **Slot** the frill onto the neck and glue to the cheeks.

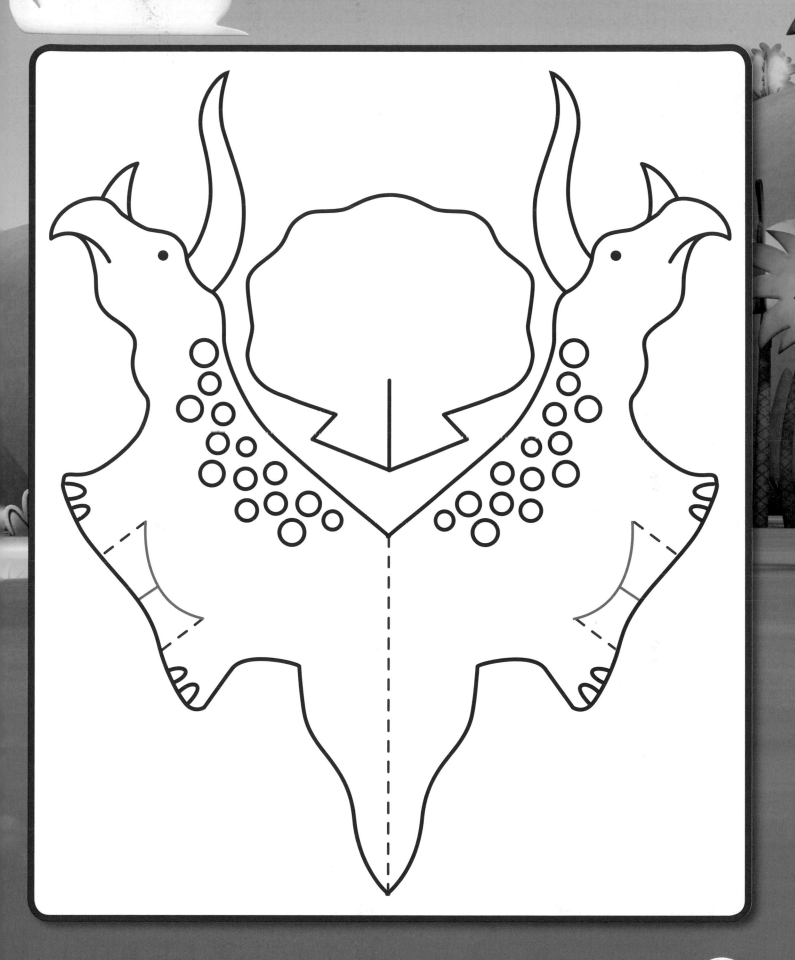

Hide-and-Seek

Some of the team are mending this brick wall. But who are they? There are 3 characters hiding here. Shout out their names as you spot them!

Answers on page 68.

Scoop's Dino Dodge

Scoop has got a lot of digging to do. He needs to get through to Bob but he can't dig where there are bones in the way. Help him find his way to Bob.

Start

Finish

Answer on page 68.

Muck's Train Trouble

 **Bob**  **train**  **dinosaur**  **Muck**  **Lofty**  **bridge**

You can help read this story. Join in when you see a picture.

 and the team were building a ride at the

 Fun Park! was digging out where

the track would go. He kept hitting big rocks.

52

But wanted to do it without help from the other

diggers. came to see if  was ready for him

to lift the track into place. But  was still

struggling with the rocks. "I don't want the other diggers

to help," he said. But kept finding bigger rocks.

"We can't build around them," he said.

"The ground is too boggy." So built a

over them. It was very wobbly.  sent a  round

the track to test it. But the  started to fall down!

The other diggers arrived just in time to help

prop up the . The went safely over!

"I did need your help after all," said . Just then,

Scratch noticed something. "These aren't rocks," he said,

"they are  bones – it's a Stegosaurus!"

Together the team dug out the rest of the

and built a strong new  over it.

The Stegosaurus **Ride** was ready!

Muck Introduces ...

This spiky guy must have been able to put up a good fight. But I wonder if he liked to play too ... Perhaps he loved mud as much as me!

These larger spikes are called plates. Can you count them?

Compared to the rest of his body his head and brain were small.

The Stegosaurus's front legs were shorter than his back ones.

the Stegosaurus

Colour in this picture of Muck. You could cover him in sticky, brown mud if you like! Let's get mucky!

Look at these fierce tail spikes!

Animal Antics

Here are just some of the animals who live around Fixham Harbour. Circle the odd one out in each row.

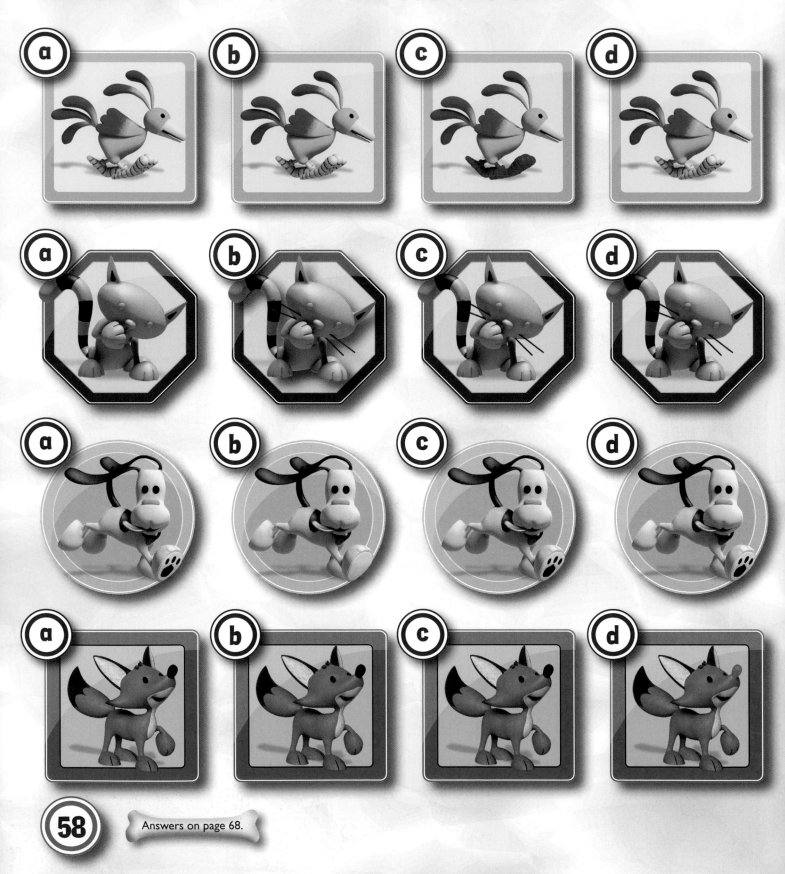

Answers on page 68.

Roller Coaster Whizz!

Use a pencil or your finger to zoom Bob along the roller coaster trail. If he falls off, go back to the beginning and try again!

Start

Finish

A Dinosaur for Scratch

"Today we're going to finish the Dinosaur Fun Park, ready for the grand opening," announced Bob to the team.

The whole team cheered, except Scratch, who looked worried.

"But that means I've only got today to find a dinosaur," he said. **"Nearly everyone's found one except me!"**

Scratch was put in charge of building the foundations for the fence. He really hoped that while he was digging he'd find a dinosaur. He dug with all his might, but didn't find anything.

Bob called the whole team over to tell them something – everyone except Scratch. Scratch thought Bob wasn't including him because he hadn't found a dinosaur yet.

But it was because Bob had a secret. The team huddled round as Bob whispered to them.

"Remember, not a word to Scratch!" said Bob.

As the team came back, Scratch said crossly, **"I'm going to find a dinosaur, just like you all have!"**

"What if we need you on the job?" asked Muck.

But Scratch had already gone!

Scratch went off to hunt for dinosaur bones. He met Spud who was looking at his big book of dinosaurs.

"Where do you think I should dig for a dinosaur?" he asked.

"Um … you should dig … there," said Spud, pointing right outside the park.

Scratch zoomed out of the park and started digging. Soon he had dug a big hole but there was no sign of any dinosaur bones.

When Bob saw the hole he was worried someone would fall in.

"Can you fill it in please, Scratch?" he asked.

But Scratch was in such a rush to find a dinosaur that he decided to fill in the hole later. He met Wendy who asked him to dig a hole for her. She pointed to where she wanted it. Scratch started to dig the hole. As he dug he thought about how much he wanted to find a dinosaur. He rushed off without finishing his work.

"Scratch has got it all backwards," said Rubble. **"It should be job first, then dinosaur …"**

A little later Bob gathered the team together.

"Now we need to dig the foundations for the special Diplodocus gate," he said. "Where's Scratch?"

Bob called him over and showed him where to start digging. "I need Scoop and Muck to help me with … er … something else."

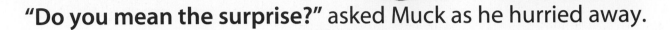

"Do you mean the surprise?" asked Muck as he hurried away.

Scratch watched them go. "I'll do this later," he said to himself. "I have to find a dinosaur first or I won't be part of the team."

Much later, Rubble came looking for Scratch. "Scratch, you've been ages," he said. "You need to come and dig the gate foundations. And just look at the size of this hole."

Scratch stopped and looked at the hole he had dug. "Oh dear, it is big," he said. "But I haven't got time to fill it in and fix everything else. What am I going to do?"

"You should really have done your job first," said Rubble. "But don't worry, I'll help you. Everything always works out in the end."

Rubble and Scratch worked hard to fill in the holes. Then Scratch got to work on the foundations. Bob was delighted to see the foundations finished.

"It's only done because Rubble helped me," admitted Scratch. "I was too busy looking for a dinosaur."

"Don't worry about looking for a dinosaur, Scratch," said Bob. "Let's get this gate built first."

Together, the team put together the Diplodocus gate.

"All the dinosaurs look amazing," said Scratch, sadly. "But I never did find one of my own."

"Come with us, Scratch," announced Bob. "We've got a surprise for you."

With his eyes closed, Scratch was led through the park.

"You can open your eyes now," said Wendy.

Scratch opened his eyes and there in front of him was the most amazing sight – a dinosaur sculpture made out of scrap metal. It looked a lot like Scratch!

"We built it just for you," said Bob. "It's your very own dinosaur."

The team decided to name the dinosaur a Scratchosaurus!

"Thank you so much," said Scratch, happily, as they all rushed off to the grand opening.

"Welcome," said Tony Toberomi, "To Fixham's very own … Dinosaur Fun Park!"

Everyone cheered. The Fun Park looked amazing and was finished on time.

"You were right, Rubble," said Scratch. "Everything does work out in the end!"

Fun Park Race!

FINISH

START

The roller coaster's rolling backwards. Go back to START.

Bark like Scruffty. Go forward 2 spaces.

Bird shows you a shortcut.

You finish the job on time. Go to FINISH.

Pretend to hammer just like Bob. Go forward 2 spaces.

You've got the wrong materials. Go back 2 spaces.

Race your way around Fixham's first Fun Park – it'll be fun from start to finish! You can play this game with a friend. You will need a dice and a counter each. You can use buttons or coins. The first person to roll a 6 starts. Take turns to roll the dice and move your counters. The first counter to cross the finish line wins!

Turn round 3 times like Dizzy. Go forward 2 spaces.

Spud has lost his book of dinosaurs. Go back 2 spaces.

Roley's hit a big rock. Go back 3 spaces.

You find a Stegosaurus skeleton. Go forward 1 space.

The bridge ahead is broken. Go back 2 spaces.

Answers

Page 17
Lofty is lifting Bob's tool box.

Page 18
There is an apple in the sky, a purple tree, Roley's eyes are red, Pilchard is yellow and Scoop has Scratch's digger.

Page 28
Shadow 4 is correct.

Page 29
Yes there are! There are 10 Bobs and 11 hammers.

Page 35
Dizzy has lost her black stripe, the centre of her wheels are yellow, her eyes are looking a different way, Bob's spanner has changed to a hammer, Bob's belt buckle is red.

Page 45
Shadow 3 is correct.

Page 46
Roley should be green.
Scoop should be yellow.
Muck should be red.
Scratch should be blue.
Dizzy should be orange.

Page 50
Bob, Wendy and Dizzy are hiding behind the wall.

Page 51

Page 58
Bird c has pink feet.
Pilchard a has no whiskers.
Scruffty b has a paw print missing.
Fox d has a pink nose.

Advertisement

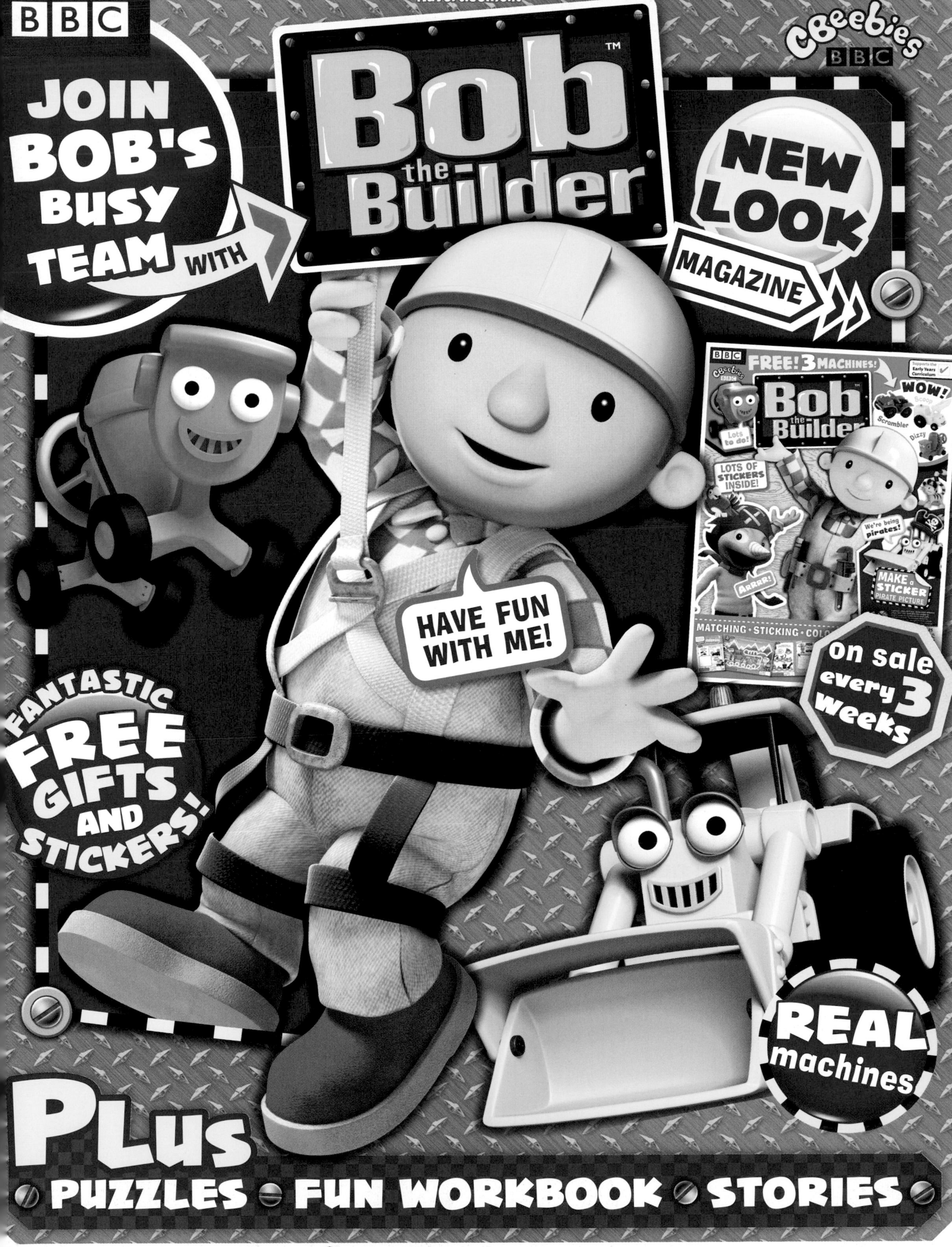